This edition published by Parragon Books Ltd in 2016

Parragon Books Ltd
Chartist House
15-17 Trim Street
Bath BA1 1HA, UK
www.parragon.com

Tiana's Friendship Fix-up written by Cynthea Liu
Illustrated by Adrienne Brown

Snow White and the Three Giants written by Cherie Gosling
Illustrated by Jordi Municio-Planas

Belle and the Perfect Pearl written by Ellen D. Risco
Illustrated by the Disney Storybook Art Team

Merida and the Perfect Pearl written by Lyra Spenser
Illustrated by IBOIX and Andrea Cagol

ISBN 978-1-4748-4606-6

Printed in China

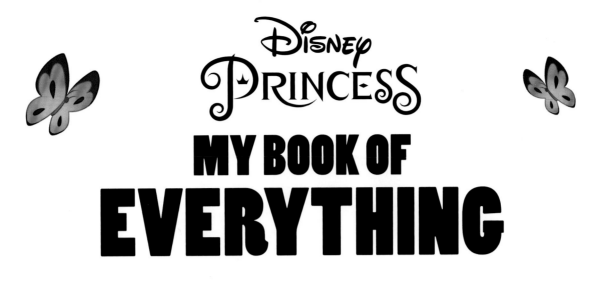

Disney PRINCESS
MY BOOK OF
EVERYTHING

Contents

PaRragon

Bath · New York · Cologne · Melbourne · Delhi
Hong Kong · Shenzhen · Singapore

Tiana's Friendship Fix-up

Charlotte rummaged through her wardrobe.
"I've got nothing new to wear, Tia. We need to
go shopping."

Tiana groaned. "I hardly have time
to sit, let alone shop, Lottie."

Charlotte pouted. "Oh, you're always so busy with your restaurant and Prince Naveen," she said. "You're my best friend, Tia. I just want to spend time with you."

Charlotte had a point. Tiana had been beyond busy. "All right," Tiana said. "We can go shopping." Then she put her fingers in her ears as Charlotte squealed in delight.

To start, Charlotte led Tiana to the
Bayou Boutique and tried on a big, pink dress.
"Isn't this darling?" Charlotte asked.

"That's swell, Lottie," Tiana replied.
"Shall we get it and go?"

But Charlotte wasn't finished.
She tried on lots more dresses before
she made up her mind.
"And there's one more thing,"
she said. "We need a dress for you!"

"But I love the dresses Mama made for me," Tiana said. "I don't need another."

"There's always room for a new dress," Charlotte said. "How about this one?"

"But, Lottie ..." Tiana said.

"This one?" Charlotte interrupted.

"Thanks, Lottie," Tiana said, hurrying
out of the shop. "I know you're trying, but
the restaurant is about to open. I have to go."

Both Tiana and Charlotte felt bad about how things had gone during their shopping trip. Neither liked disappointing the other. So, the next day, they apologized.

"Phew, I'm glad that's over," Charlotte said, "because I have another brilliant idea about how we can spend time together!"

"I'll help you!" Charlotte said. "Won't that be fun?"
Tiana wasn't so sure, but she thought she should at least give it a try. She showed Charlotte how to make beignets –

– and Charlotte did a great job. "Can you handle making the rest?" asked Tiana.

"Is my daddy's name Big Daddy?" Charlotte said.

After Tiana left, Charlotte heated up a pan of oil. Soon it was time to fry the dough. She dropped each one in and –

Whoooosh! After the smoke cleared,
Tiana saw the beignets. "Oh, Lottie!
What did you do?"
Charlotte couldn't explain herself.
This wasn't how she wanted things to go.
She started to cry.

When she got home, Charlotte moaned.

She complained.

But most of all, she missed her best friend.

Meanwhile, Tiana grimaced.

She grumbled.

Then she missed her best friend, too.

That night, both Charlotte and Tiana knew they had to find each other.
Tiana spotted Charlotte in front of the bright lights of the theatre.

They hugged. "I'm sorry," Charlotte cried.
"Me, too," Tiana said. "I want to spend time with you,
Lottie, but maybe shopping or cooking isn't it."

"I agree," Charlotte said.
"So what can we do?"

"Why don't we see a show?" Tiana suggested. "It's one of our favourites!"

"I think that's a wonderful idea," Charlotte said.

After the show, Tiana said, "That was amazing."

"Indeed!" Charlotte smiled. "But the way your mama told the story when we were girls is still the best."

Tiana knew she and Charlotte wouldn't agree with each other all the time, but they'd always agree on what mattered: being best friends forever!

DISNEY PRINCESS

Snow White and the Three Giants

$\mathcal{S}$ince meeting the Dwarfs long ago, Snow White knew the path to their cottage well. But one day, she was so busy talking to the woodland creatures, she took a wrong turn.

She arrived at a very different cottage instead.

At first, Snow White didn't notice …

… but then she stepped inside.
"Oh my!" Snow White exclaimed.

Instead of a neat row of seven little
chairs, she saw three enormous chairs.

Instead of the cosy kitchen she knew so well,
a fire roared and crackled in an enormous hearth.
Then, just as Snow White discovered the
enormous dining table, the ground began to shake.

"Oh no!" she gasped.

With a groan, the door opened
and in came three of the tallest people
Snow White had ever seen in her life.
They lumbered straight toward her.

What should I do now?
thought Snow White.

Snow White cleared her throat and stepped into view.
"Excuse me," she said.

The giants jumped back in surprise.

"I'm sorry," Snow White continued,
"I let myself in by mistake."

"Oh!" said the largest giant. "You scared us. We don't get visitors often."

"But now that you're here," said the least-big giant, "you should join us for dinner."

The least-big giant helped Snow White climb up on to his chair. "You'll need some cushions," he said.

"And here is a small plate and a glass," said the middle-sized giant.

"Thank you," said Snow White.
"You're all so kind!"

The next day, back at home, Snow White
told the Dwarfs about her adventures.
"G-G-Giants?!" stammered Bashful.
Sleepy yawned. "Aren't they dangerous?"
"Not at all," Snow White replied.

"Don't trust them!" Grumpy said.
"You can't trust anyone that tall."

"But I'm taller than you, and you trust me!"
Snow White said. "Well, you'll just have to meet
them and see for yourself."

Back at the castle, Snow White wrote 10 party
invitations and made a list of the delicious food she'd make.
All she needed now was a fun party game....

On the day of the party, Snow White announced,
"We're going to play Snap. I'll point out something
about me, and if it's true for you, shout 'Snap!'
And then it's someone else's turn."

"Oh, I love games like this," chuckled Doc.

"Here we go," said Snow White, thinking for a moment.

"I have two eyes."

"Snap!" yelled the Dwarfs.
"Snap!" yelled the giants.

Snow White turned to Bashful, who was up next.
"Um, I have two ears."
"Snap!" called the Dwarfs. "Snap!" called the giants.
It was the largest giant's turn.

"Ahem, I have one nose."

"Snap!" shouted the Dwarfs.
"Snap!" shouted the giants.

"I guess we have a lot in common
after all," Grumpy muttered.

"Yes, you do!" said Snow White.
"And there's one more thing you have
in common ... you are all my friends!"

Disney PRINCESS

Enchanting Activities

Complete these princess puzzles and activities,
then turn to page 100 for the answers.

"Magic Mirror on the wall, who is the fairest one of all?"
Draw yourself in the mirror.

Doc and Dopey are making a necklace for Snow White.
Can you colour it?

1 = RED   2 = YELLOW   3 = BLUE

Hi ho, hi ho. Who is off to work?
Cross out all the 'I's and 'T's to find out.

1. TDIOIPTEIY   _____
2. IBTASITIHTFIUL   _____
3. STINEETZIY   _____
4. TSLIETEPTIY   _____
5. IHTAIIPTPIY   _____
6. IGRTIUMTPIY   _____
7. TDIITOTIICT   _____

Look at this picture of Snow White and her forest friends. Then answer the questions below.

1. How many birds? _____

2. How many butterflies? _____

3. How many rabbits? _____

4. How many squirrels? _____

5. How many turtles? _____

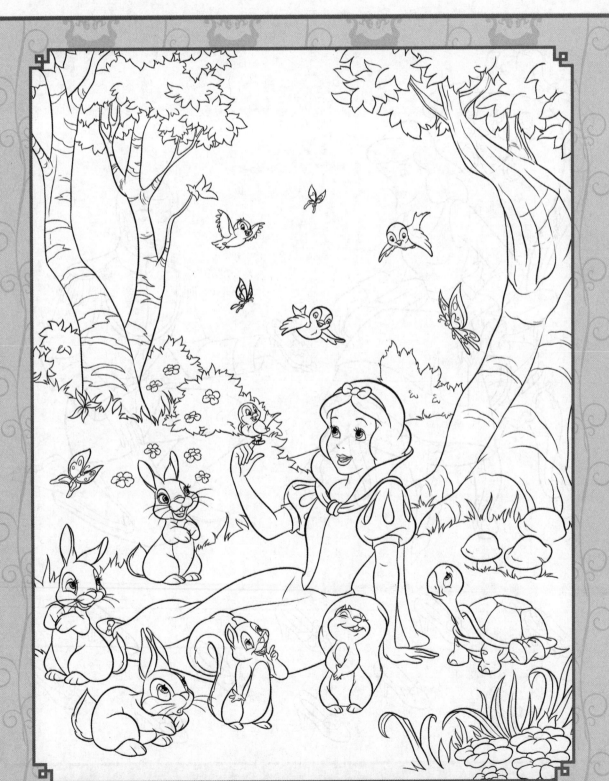

Help the Prince find the missing glass slipper. Circle the slipper that matches the one in the Prince's hand.

Draw a picture of yourself at the ball.

Prince Charming's Ball

Find the following words in the pumpkin carriage below.
(Hint: You will find the words going down and across.)

Cinderella
prince
slipper
Gus
midnight
mice
pumpkin
ball
stepmother
gown

a	s	t	d	p	r	s	e	m	g
r	m	u	d	r	i	t	i	n	n
t	p	r	i	n	c	e	d	r	r
s	p	u	m	t	r	p	i	n	s
g	u	s	a	s	s	m	n	i	l
o	m	i	c	e	r	o	i	g	a
w	p	b	a	l	l	t	g	h	i
n	k	r	s	t	m	h	h	t	e
c	i	n	d	e	r	e	l	l	a
r	n	m	p	d	u	r	p	r	w

Help Cinderella's friends finish the surprise! Colour the dress pink, the stars yellow and the hearts purple.

Can you match these sentences with the pictures they describe? Write the number of each sentence in the circle beside the correct picture.

3) Cinderella's friends help her get dressed.

2) The Fairy Godmother comforts Cinderella.

1) The shoe fits!

Help Prince Phillip save Princess Aurora.
Connect the dots to reveal his magic sword.

Help Prince Phillip find his way to the castle so
he can awaken Princess Aurora with a kiss.

START

FINISH

What gifts do the fairies give to Princess Aurora when she is a baby? Use the code below to find out.

A	B	C	D	E	F	G	H	I	J	K	L	M	N	O	P	Q	R	S	T	U	V	W	X	Y	Z
1	2	3	4	5	6	7	8	9	10	11	12	13	14	15	16	17	18	19	20	21	22	23	24	25	26

Flora gives the gift of _____.

2	5	1	21	20	25

Fauna gives the gift of _____.

19	15	14	7

Number these pictures in the order they happened.

Connect the dots to see Briar Rose's dance partner.

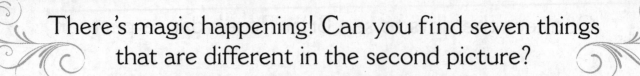

There's magic happening! Can you find seven things that are different in the second picture?

Use crayons or pens to colour Ariel, Flounder and Sebastian.

Look at this picture of Ariel, Eric and their animal friends.
Then answer the questions below.

1. How many seagulls? _____

2. How many frogs? _____

3. How many fish? _____

4. How many flamingos? _____

Join Ariel as she explores the shipwreck!
Look for the names listed on the right in the puzzle below.
(Hint: You will find them going down and across.)

Prince Eric
Ariel
Flounder
King Triton
Max
Scuttle
Sebastian
Ursula

```
k r s e a d t c g m p
i e p a z u l l r a r
n o u r s u l a r f i
g d n i u o s s y l n
t e r e p a c r w o c
r l a l d n u o d u e
i s e b a s t i a n e
t d p r e g t s e d r
o r m a x p l t n e i
n i n c s s e d w r c
```

Eric and Ariel are collecting shells, stones and sticks on the beach. They've arranged them in two different patterns. Can you finish each pattern by filling in the blank spaces with shells, stones or sticks?

Everyone in the kitchen wants to cheer Belle up with a show.
Find the matching dishes, cups, forks and knives.
Circle the ones that are the same.

There are seven odd and silly things happening in this picture. Can you find them all? Here are some hints:

- What's Gaston wearing on his head?
- There's a fire somewhere.
- Someone is walking on his hands.
- What an odd-looking bicycle.
- Take a look at Gaston's feet.
- It looks like Belle is going swimming!
- An animal has escaped from the farm!

Be a reader like Belle! Ask an adult to help
you cut along the dotted lines to create two bookmarks.

Let's read
a story
together!

Reading can
take you to
far-off places!

© Disney

© Disney

Help Belle and the Beast build a snowman with eyes, arms, a nose and a mouth. Don't forget his hat and scarf!

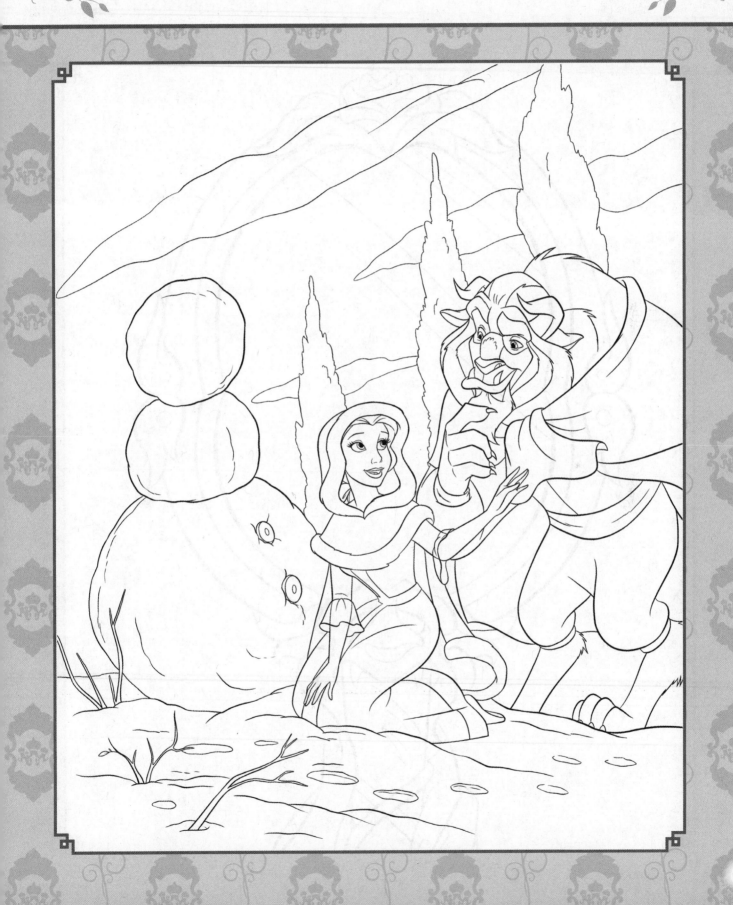

The Beast's Magic Mirror lets you see anyone you want.
Draw the person you would like to see in the Magic Mirror.

Write the names of the objects below in the crossword puzzle.

Across

1   4   6   7   8

Down

2   3   4   5

Can you find the following 10 objects hidden in the picture below?

- A glove
- A beach ball
- A cockerel
- A handbag
- A brush
- A cake
- A broom
- A pair of boots
- A comb
- A car

What kind of pet do Jasmine and Aladdin have?
Cross out all the 'u's and 'b's to find the answer to the riddle.

bau ufublubuyiunbg bucuabur-bupubuetb!

Use crayons or colouring pencils to colour
the palace and the city of Agrabah.

Jasmine and Aladdin are ready for a reading adventure!
Ask an adult to help you cut along the dotted lines
to create two bookmarks.

Read a book and discover a whole new world!

Every book holds a new adventure!

Jasmine wore the same outfit and accessories twice this week.
Which two days did she wear the same things?
_____ and _____

Tuesday   Wednesday   Thursday

Monday

Friday   Saturday   Sunday

Look at this picture of Pocahontas, John Smith and their woodland friends. Then answer the questions below.

1. How many deer? _____   3. How many rabbits? _____

2. How many squirrels? _____   4. How many raccoons? _____

FINISH

START

How many butterflies do you see in the picture?
Write the number below.

I see _____ butterflies.

Meeko is hidden four times in the picture below. Can you find him?

One of the canoes below matches Pocahontas's canoe. Which one is it?

a

b

c

d

e

Write the names of the animals and objects below in the crossword puzzle.

Across

2

5

6

Down

1

3

4

Mulan needs to get to the Emperor. Can you help her?

START

FINISH

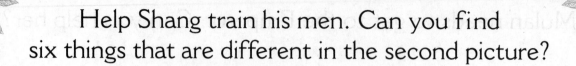

Help Shang train his men. Can you find
six things that are different in the second picture?

Complete this scene with the small pictures below.
Write the letter of each picture in the correct white box.

A

B

C

Help the Matchmaker find the two Mulans who are the same.

Write the names of the people and things below in the crossword puzzle.

Across

3 5 7

Down

1 2 4 6

Each of the rows below must have four princesses:
Snow White, Aurora, Cinderella and Belle.
Fill each empty box with the correct letter.

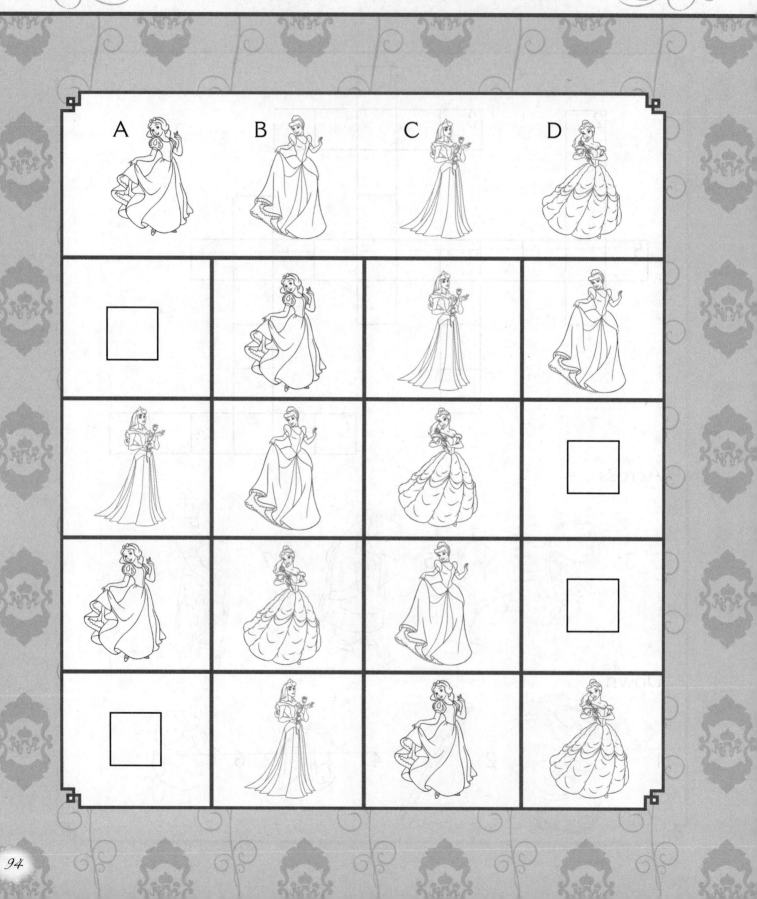

Ask an adult help you cut out each picture, punch a hole at the top and thread a ribbon through the hole. Then decorate your room with these beautiful princesses!

Draw a picture of yourself as a princess on the back of the decorations.

© Disney

© Disney

© Disney

© Disney

Ask an adult to help you cut out each picture, punch a hole at the top and thread a ribbon through the hole. Then decorate your room with these beautiful princesses!

Draw a picture of yourself as a princess on the back of the decorations.

© Disney

© Disney

© Disney

© Disney

Draw a line from each princess to her shadow.

Answers

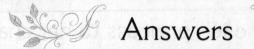

Page 52

1. Dopey, 2. Bashful,
3. Sneezy, 4. Sleepy,
5. Happy, 6. Grumpy,
7. Doc.

Page 53

1. 4 birds, 2. 4 butterflies,
3. 3 rabbits, 4. 2 squirrels,
5. 1 turtle.

Page 54

Page 56

Page 58

Page 60

Page 61

Flora gives the gift of BEAUTY.
Fauna gives the gift of SONG.

Page 62

Page 64

Page 66

1. 2 seagulls, 2. 3 frogs,
3. 4 fish, 4. 3 flamingos.

Page 67

Page 68

Page 69

Page 70

Page 75

Page 76

Page 77

A flying car-pet.

Page 81

Tuesday and Thursday.

Page 82

1. 3 deer, 2. 4 squirrels,
3. 2 rabbits, 4. 1 raccoon.

Page 83

Page 84

I see 22 butterflies.

Page 85

Page 86

Page 87

C matches Pocahontas's canoe.

Page 88

Page 89

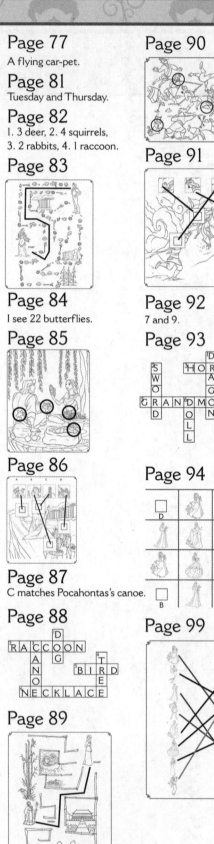

Page 90

Page 91

Page 92

7 and 9.

Page 93

Page 94

Page 99

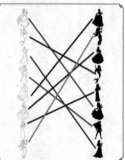

100

Disney
PRINCESS

Beautiful Colouring

Use your favourite colouring pens or crayons to
make these princess pictures look magical.

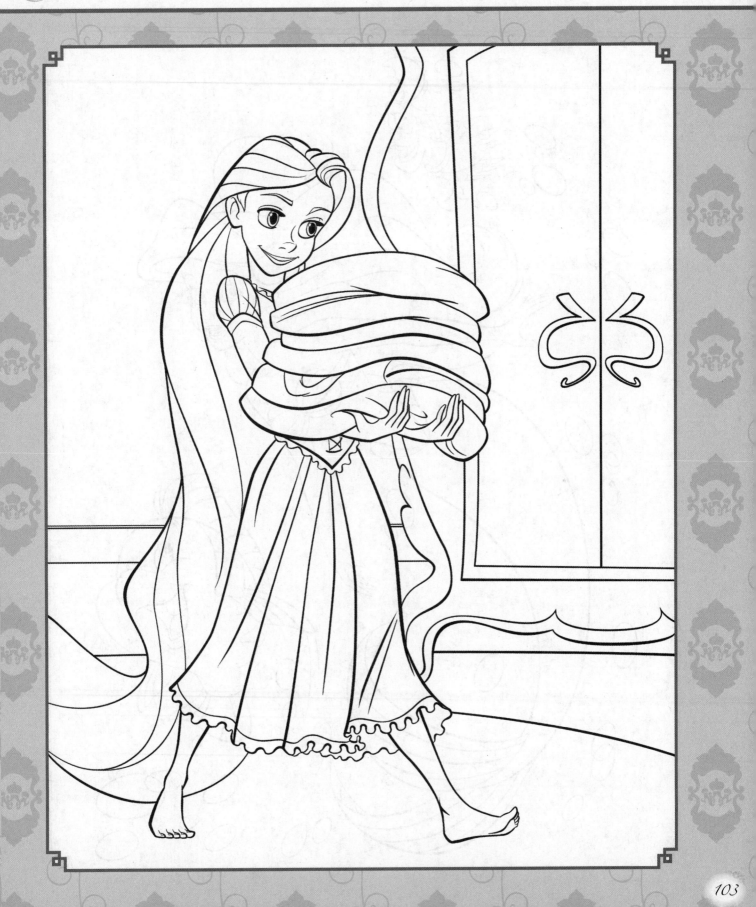

Ariel and Flounder meet some friendly whales.

Grumpy just can't help being
a bit grumpy sometimes!

Snow White meets the three
friendly giants for the first time.

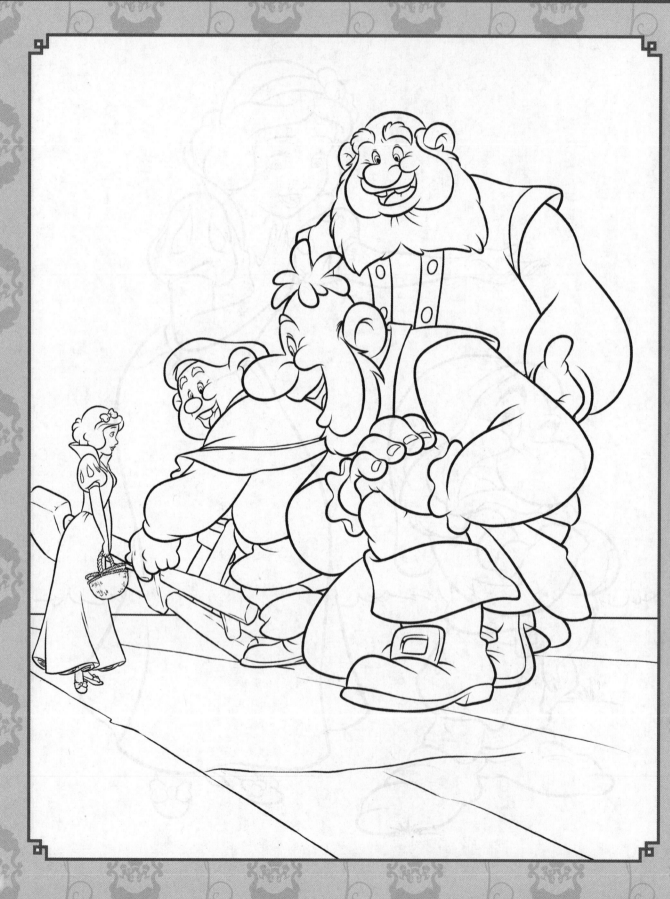

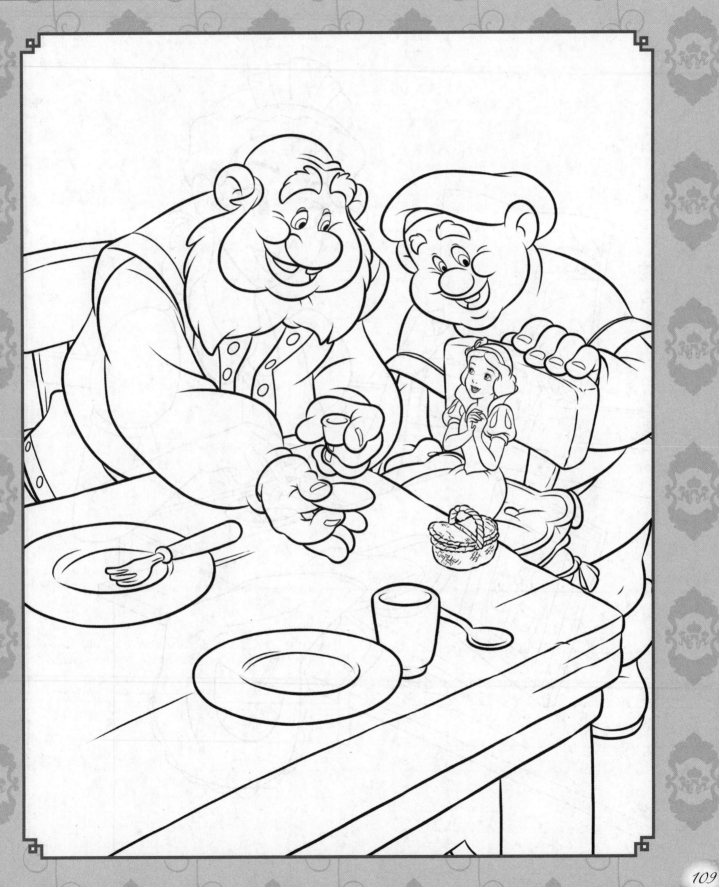

Tiana dreams of owning her own restaurant.

Tiana works hard to achieve her dreams.

Belle reads to the children of the village.

Belle likes to ride with Philippe through the woods.

The Dwarfs learn many things from Snow White.

Snow White helps a little turtle
who has fallen over.

Merida is the best archer in the kingdom.

Merida hates it when her mum, Queen Elinor, brushes her hair.

Flounder cares for his friend Ariel very much.

Ariel's friends are always playing around.

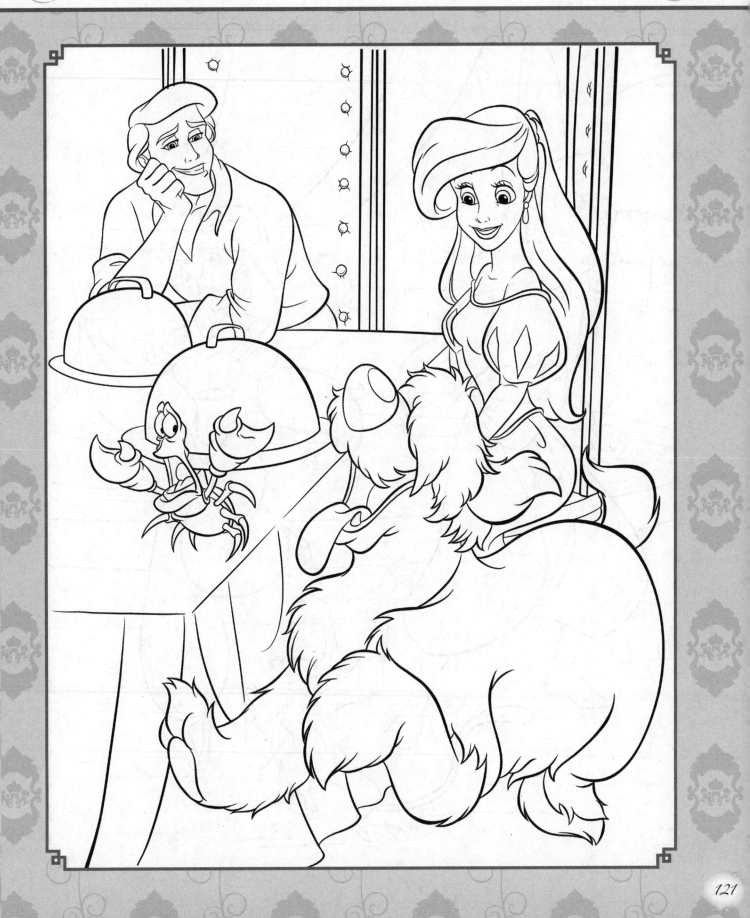

Aladdin and Jasmine monkey around with Abu.

Jasmine and Aladdin try to count all the stars.

Aurora arrives home after a walk in the woods.

Aurora adds small sugar roses to a birthday cake.

Charlotte lends one of her pretty dresses to Tiana.

Tiana looks like a princess.

Belle loves her father very much.

The Prince and Belle read their favourite book together.

Cinderella has made a special treat for Jaq's birthday.

Cinderella has decided what kind of pie to make.

Music is the language of the heart!

Snow White's woodland friends join her for a walk.

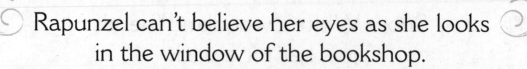

Rapunzel can't believe her eyes as she looks
in the window of the bookshop.

Rapunzel and Flynn share a quiet moment
on the lake as they wait for the floating lights.

Merida can't move in her formal dress!

Merida is a talented archer.

Jasmine is lucky to have a good friend like Rajah.

The Genie always makes Jasmine's day.

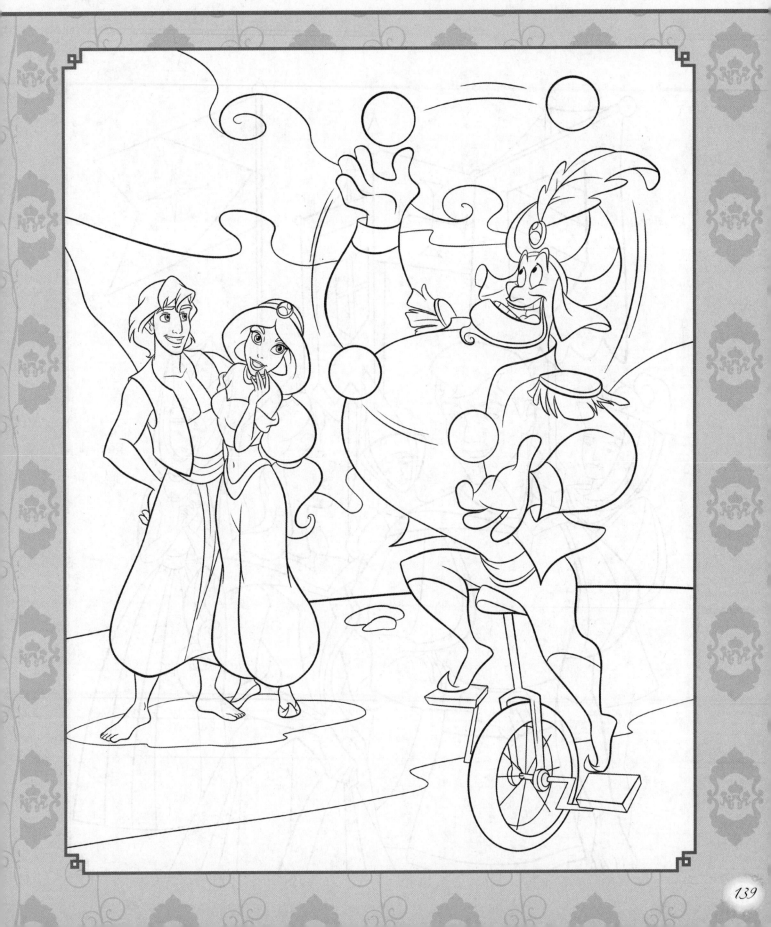

Everyone in the kingdom celebrates Aurora's birthday.

Let's get ready for a picnic!

Charlotte and Tiana have been best friends
since they were little girls.

Charlotte just adores shopping!

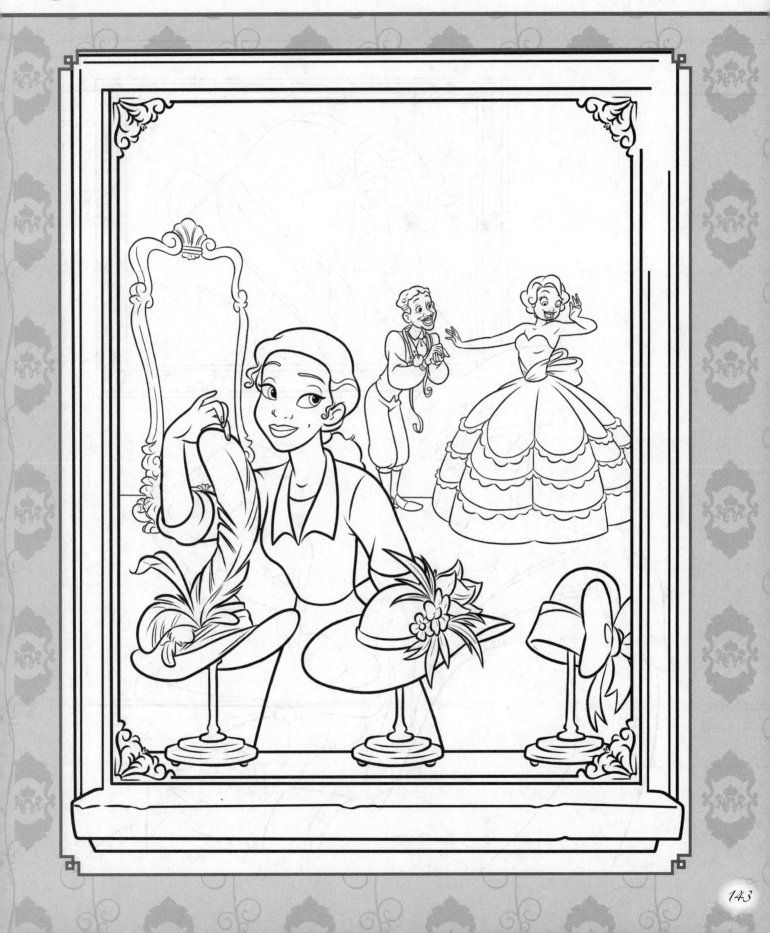

Belle's love broke the spell on the Beast and turned him back into a handsome prince.

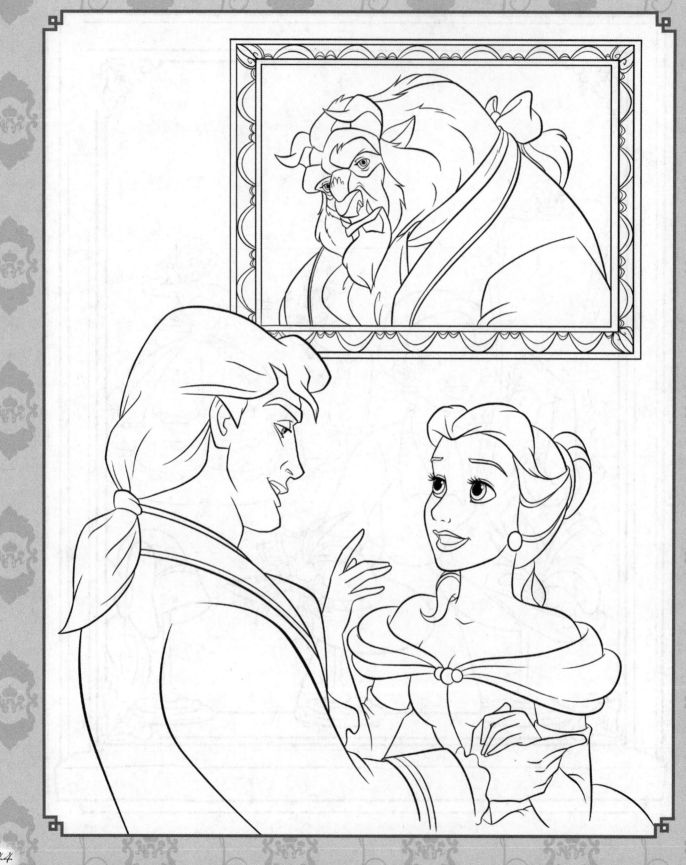

There are lots of things for Belle to buy
at the market.

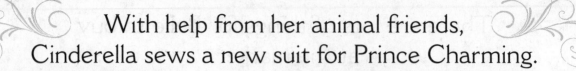

With help from her animal friends,
Cinderella sews a new suit for Prince Charming.

Cinderella's favourite vegetables are broccoli and tomatoes.

There are so many apples ready for picking!

Rapunzel is filled with wonder as she looks
at the floating lights up close for the very first time.

Flynn and Rapunzel launch their own lantern into the sky.

Ariel will never forget her life under the sea.

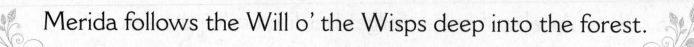

Merida follows the Will o' the Wisps deep into the forest.

Merida's favourite thing to do is ride with
Angus through the forest.

The Dwarfs and giants discover that they
have lots of things in common!

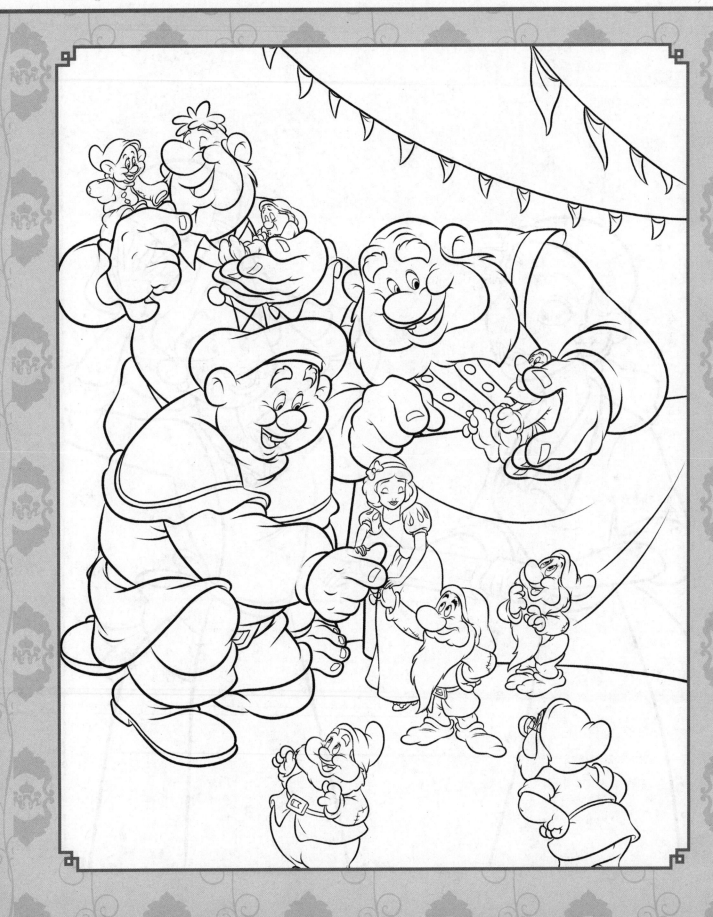

Belle keeps a diary of her happy memories.

Belle wonders what to buy Chip
for his birthday.

Cinderella remembers the ball
and how she lost one slipper.

Cinderella gives Major a treat.

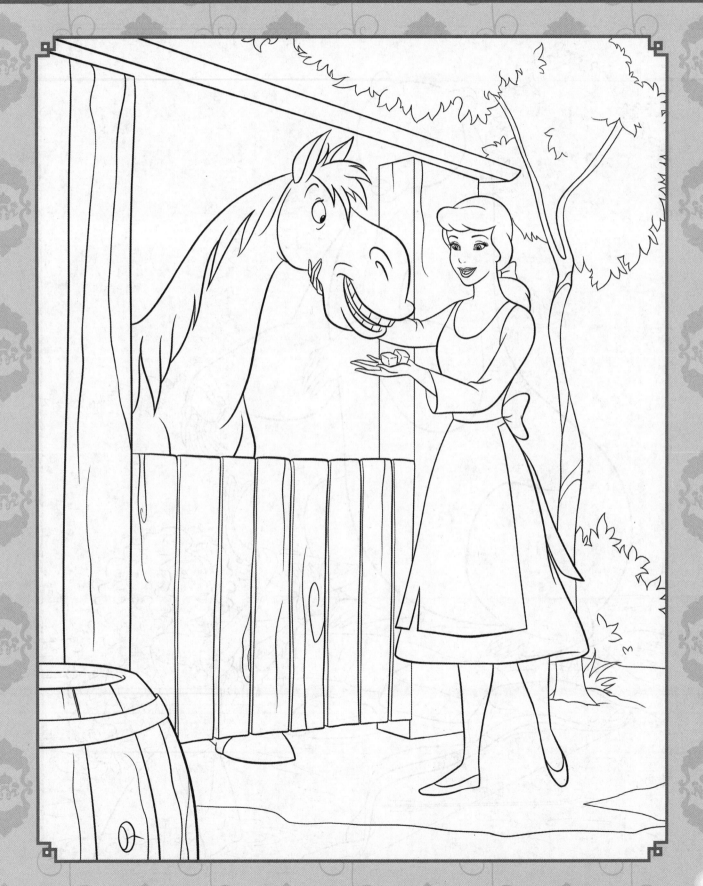

Merida is teaching Elinor-bear to fish.

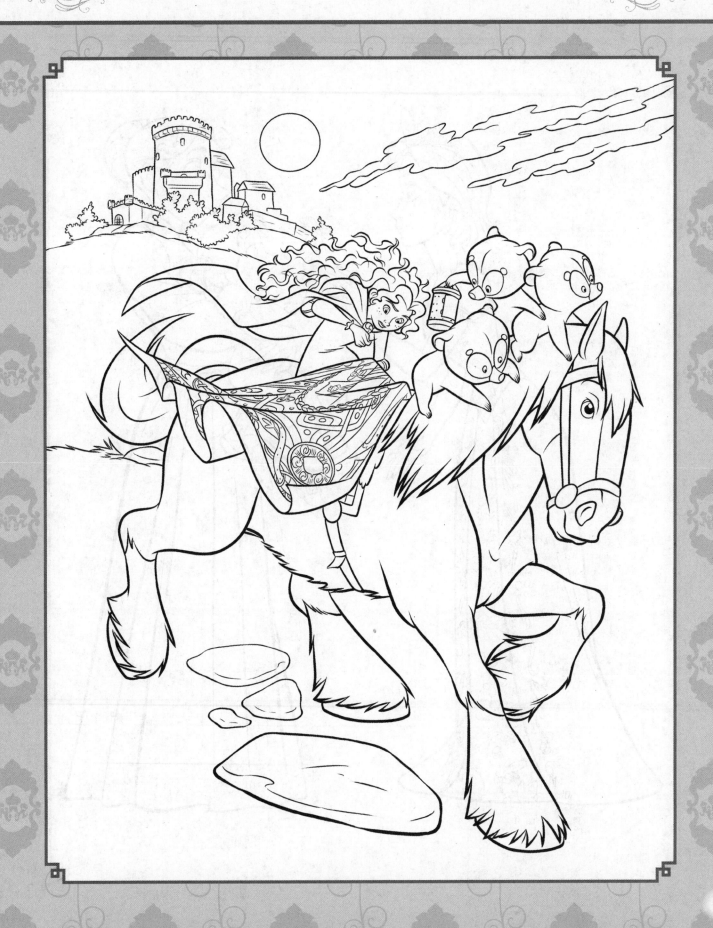

Everyone is anxious to meet Rapunzel.

As a reformed thief, Flynn sheepishly returns
the crown to its rightful owner.

Ariel and Flounder love to swim together.

Sebastian and his band give a wonderful concert!

The Sultan loves to see Jasmine being happy.

You can see the whole city from the Flying Carpet!

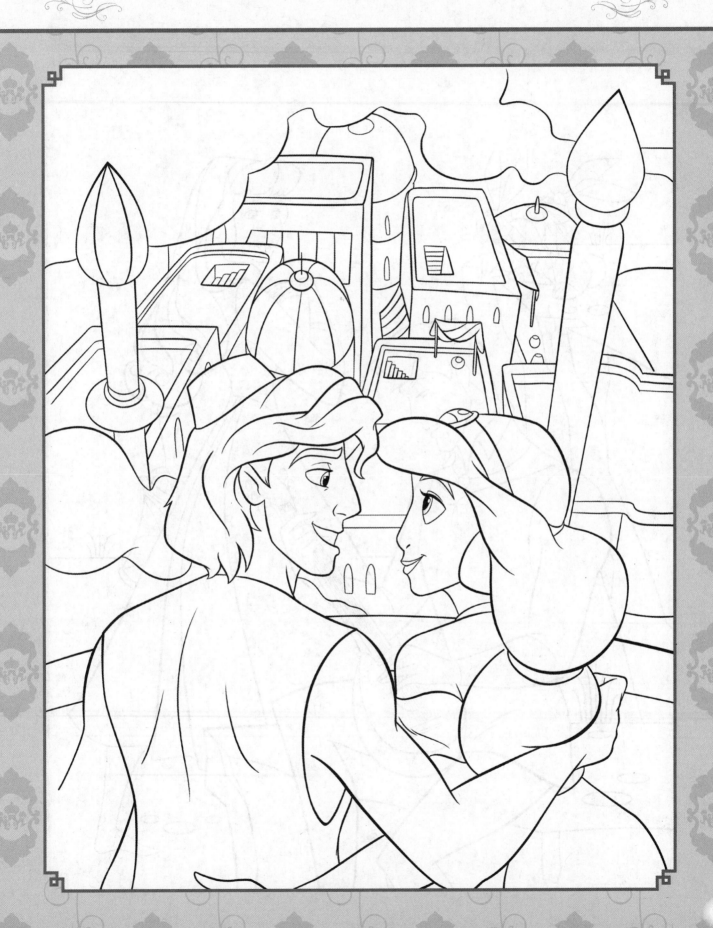

Aurora loves listening to music.

Prince Charming and Cinderella
take Bruno for a brisk walk.

The Fairy Godmother joins
Cinderella for tea and a chat.

The Dwarfs give Snow White
a beautiful sparkling diamond.

Belle and the
Perfect Pearl

"What do you suppose is behind these doors, Chip?" Belle asked the enchanted teacup.

"Books!" Chip replied.

Belle threw open the doors. "I knew it. More beautiful adventures – tucked away and forgotten!" she said.

It wasn't that the Beast didn't use the library. But when he did, he always read the same book.

"My library is your library," the Beast liked to remind Belle. "Read and enjoy any book you find."

It hadn't been long since Belle had agreed to stay at the castle in return for her father's freedom. But each day she was getting to know the Beast better. She was starting to think that he actually cared about her happiness.

So Belle took the Beast at his word and made herself at home in the library. On many days, she spent hours there, reading book after book, losing all track of time.

Belle considered books priceless treasures. So when she took a break from reading, she gave the books special attention. Belle asked Featherduster to help her dust them.

She placed fallen books back on the shelves.

She pressed flat any folded pages.

One morning, Belle noticed the Beast had left his
favourite book lying open on the arm of his chair.
"That's not good for the binding," Belle said.

She picked up the book, closed it, then turned it over in her hands. Although the leather cover was worn, it was a beautiful volume with decorative gems on its brass clasp.

"Chip, look!" she said, pointing at the pearls. There was an empty hole where a fourth one should be.

Hmmm, thought Belle. *How long has it been missing?*

Belle looked around on the floor, in case it had only just fallen out.

Chip helped her search. "I found something!" he called. There by the library door was a single, perfect pearl.

"Let's see if it fits," Belle suggested.

She dropped the pearl
into the hole in the clasp.
"Just right!" said Chip.

But the pearl was loose and wouldn't stay put.

"I have an idea," Belle said. "This book is obviously your master's favourite. I'll fix it up a bit at a time. As the finishing touch, I'll reattach the pearl."

"Then you can surprise him!" Chip cried.

Belle nodded. She was happy to do something nice for the Beast.

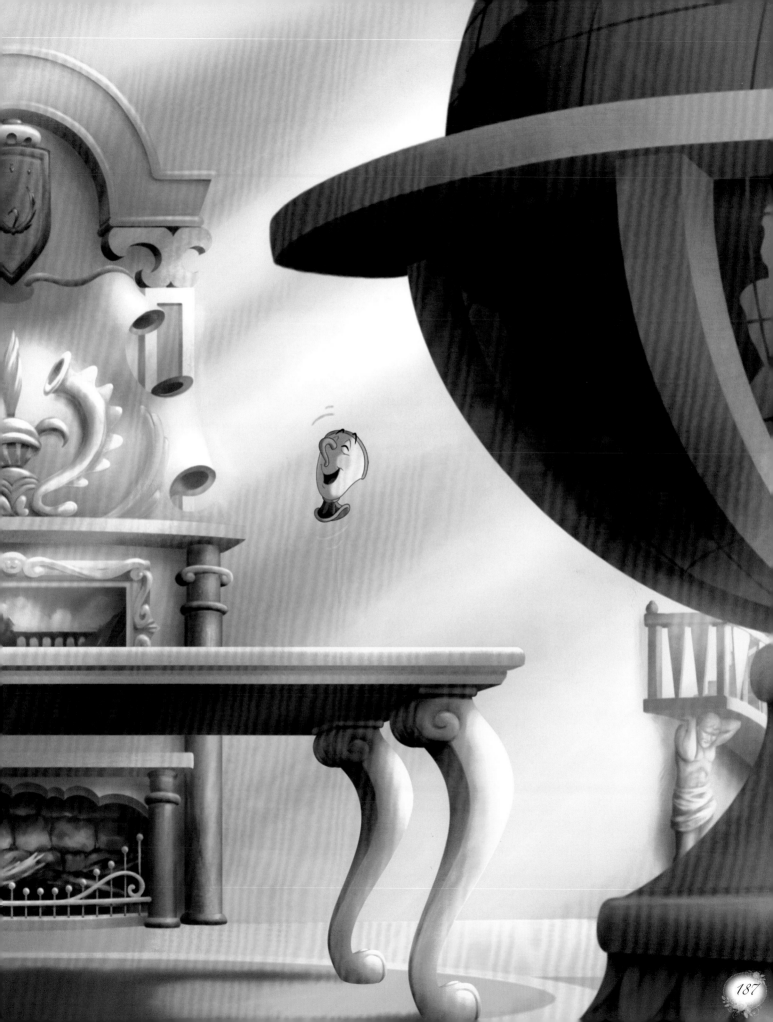

Belle got right to work. She borrowed some rags and polish from Mrs Potts and gently cleaned the leather cover. Then she put the book back on the Beast's chair so he wouldn't miss it.

But when the Beast came into the library, he didn't pick up his book. He seemed to be looking for something.

"Can I help?" Belle asked.

"NO!" he bellowed. Then, more quietly, he added, "I mean, no. Excuse me." Without another word, he left the room.

Belle was startled but shrugged it off, assuming the Beast's bad mood would pass.

That afternoon, Belle did some
more work on the book. Carefully,
she smoothed out rumpled pages and
polished the brass clasp.

"I can see myself!" Chip said.

Again, Belle put the book back in
its place on the Beast's chair.

The Ugly
Duckling

Later that evening, Belle passed the Beast in the hall. She smiled and stopped to greet him. "Good evening –"

"Good night!" he snapped, hurrying by.

Belle stood there, a bit stunned. He hadn't even glanced her way.

Is something the matter? she wondered.

The Ugly Duckling

The next morning, it was time for Belle to add the pearl. But she wasn't sure she was ready to give the book to the Beast. He had been so grouchy the day before.

What will he be like today? she wondered.

Just then, the Beast burst through the door. "You?" he cried. "You've had the pearl all along? I've been everywhere trying to find it!"

"Well, why didn't you say so!" Belle shouted, then she tossed the pearl on to the table. "By the way, I've been repairing your book as a surprise."

The Beast was shocked.
He looked at the book. He picked
up the pearl. Then he smiled – and
began to laugh.

Belle stormed towards the door.

195

"Belle, wait," the Beast said. His gentle voice made Belle stop and turn. "I've been working on something for you, too."

In the Beast's hand was a lovely antique pin. "It's been in my family a long time," he explained. "I wanted you to have it. But first, I had something to add."

He placed the pearl on the pin, at the base of the rose. It fitted perfectly.

"I removed the pearl from my book yesterday,"
he said. "But I must have dropped it on my way out
and –" He looked down. "I'm sorry I blamed you."

Now it was Belle's turn to laugh. "Well, I'm sorry
I stole your surprise."

Belle pinned the gold rose with the perfect pearl to her dress. Then she watched as the Beast noticed his book's shining brass clasp, polished cover and smooth pages.

"Thank you, Belle," he said. "You've made it new."

Belle and the Beast still had much to learn about one another. But their hearts were in the right place.

Merida and the
Missing Gem

"*A*ch!" Merida complained. "I spent all month working on a fancy brooch for Mum. But her birthday's tomorrow and it's still not right!"

Maudie clucked in sympathy, but didn't reply. As cook and nursemaid at Castle DunBroch, she was more worried about her latest batch of hot muffins.

"Mm! Who are those for?" asked Merida.

"Don't touch! These are for the DunBroch Brownie, the wee elf that lives outside the gate. He keeps things right in our castle," Maudie replied.

"Have you ever seen him?"

"Brownies don't like to be seen by humans," explained Maudie.

"But every day I leave him muffins, milk – and thistles for good luck. If the Brownie isn't happy, who knows what mischief he could make? Especially with the queen's birthday tomorrow."

Merida sighed again, thinking about her mum's birthday.

The brooch had started as a good idea. Merida chose a beautiful smoky quartz, her mother's favourite gem.

Then she designed the setting herself.

But when it was all put together, it didn't seem right.

Maybe, she thought, she should take another look at the gem....

But it was gone!

Then Merida saw
her brothers' guilty faces.
The wee devils must
have taken it!

Merida quickly realized what had happened.
Her brothers hadn't meant to cause trouble.
They'd only 'borrowed' the brooch because it
had looked so royal on their capes.

But somehow, as they played, the brooch had become lost.

"Oh, come now lads!" said Merida. "You must have dropped it somewhere. Think!"

Merida looked more closely at Hubert's shirt.

"Is this a thistle?" she asked. Then she looked at the others. "Are those crumbs on your shoes? Is that milk on your face?"

Suddenly, Merida had a very good idea where the triplets had been playing that morning.

Merida led the boys down near the gate, under the bridge, to a large, flat rock.

"Just as I thought," Merida said. "You ate the treats that Maudie made for the DunBroch Brownie!" She nodded. "So now we know where you lost the gem."

Merida and her brothers looked all around the clearing ... but they couldn't find the brooch.

Merida had another thought. "What if the Brownie took the brooch because you three ate his treats? Maudie said he makes mischief if he isn't taken care of."

Quickly, she gave each of the boys different tasks.

Hamish got more muffins.

Hubert got more milk.

Harris got more thistles.

And Merida tidied up the clearing.

Merida set up the tray and rearranged the
thistle bouquet.

The boys looked at each other. They weren't
so sure about Brownies.

But Merida had no doubts. She told her brothers to hide and be still.
Nothing happened.

Then Merida remembered that Brownies don't like humans to see them. So she tried something else.

"DunBroch Brownie," Merida whispered
into the air, "we're sorry your treats were taken!
But we tried to fix everything. Could you help us,
in return?"

There was only silence. Finally, they opened their eyes. And then Harris spotted something shiny in the crook of a tree – it was the brooch! Had the Brownie really just returned it? Or had it been there the whole time?

And even stranger, when Merida examined the gem more closely, she saw that something was very different about it.

The next evening, Merida presented the birthday brooch to her mother.

"My favourite gem, set in a silver thistle!" Elinor exclaimed. "What better luck could I have than to have you as my daughter?"

Beaming, Merida knew that everything was set right, and things were positively ... perfect.